THEATRE IN EDUCATION SERIES
Edited by John Andrews and Ossia Trilling

PIRATES CAN'T BE GENTLEMEN

Pirates Can't Be Gentlemen

by

JEAN M. THORPE

London

DENNIS DOBSON LIMITED

12 PARK PLACE   ST JAMES'S   SW1

08344370

Permission to produce this play must be obtained from:
Dennis Dobson Limited, 12 Park Place, St James's, London,
SW1. Telephone REGent 6144.

ROYALTIES: *Amateur and School Productions* £1 1 0 for
every performance.

Professional or Children's Theatre Productions
by arrangement with the publishers.

First published in Great Britain in MCML by Dennis
Dobson Limited. All rights reserved. Printed in Great
Britain by G. F. Tomkin Limited, London, E11.
805 (175)/R

PREFACE

AFTER I HAD asked a small class of Secondary School girls, ten- and eleven-year-olds, what sort of play they would like to act, I decided that the simplest way of satisfying their demands was to write the play myself. This I did, subjecting it, act by act, to their criticism, clarifying or cutting out anything that seemed beyond their comprehension and fulfilling as many of their wishes as possible.

This, then, is a play with several 'big parts', and even the minor characters appear fairly often and can assume definite personalities, and contribute much to the success of the play by their silent acting. Trickery seemed to appeal to the children's sense of humour, especially when it was employed by children against grown-ups and in defence of right. The cabin-boy's gaucheries made his a coveted part, but I noticed that all the actors grew attached to their own characters. I tried to keep the story within what seemed to them the bounds of possibility.

A 'costume' play was, according to my clients, imperative, but, remembering the difficulties of these days, I decided that the costumes must be adaptable from existing stocks in the school acting-cupboard and everyday garments. Period did not matter much. The girls in the play were put into long 'Greenaway' frocks and Robert wore knee breeches, a shirt and cravat. The pirates were easy to dress, even though girls. Coloured handkerchiefs covered long hair; ear-rings, daggers and make-up gave the necessary swagger, while a black eye-shade rejoiced the heart of Patch. Some wore shirts and long baggy trousers, loose over bare feet or tucked into Wellington boots. One wore a tunic, one was a long-robed Moor, and the Captain and Mate boasted full Tudor-ish trunks and skirted coats. (We made our 'Property men' into pirates too, and let them add to the crowd in Act III.) The Mate's best cummerbund was an old piece of stuff, painted gaily, inked in the middle where the stain would not show till it was removed, and slit just before his entrance in Act II.

Properties, too, had to be simple. We acted without scenery, but we made bushes of branches, cut, and thrust into camouflaged waste-paper baskets. The impression of a camp was given by the bundles of rugs, stools, cooking-utensils, etc., that the pirates carried on to the stage themselves, to dump beside the empty crate or make the captain's bed.

Originally, the play was intended chiefly for the enjoyment of the actors themselves. But their zest and success in the actual performance, and the kindly appreciation of the school audience, persuaded me that the play might give pleasure to other groups of actors, girls, or girls and boys, of the same age or older, and to other audiences.

JEAN M. THORPE

CHARACTERS IN ORDER OF APPEARANCE

BEN, Cabin-boy

TOUGH TOM, Bo'sun

LOOPY ⎫
PATCH ⎭ Pirates

PIRATE CAPTAIN

MATE

SARAH MIRANDA COURTIER

ROBERT MAINWARING

PRISCILLA MAINWARING

ALICE MAINWARING

SCENE: Scrub on the uninhabited end of an Atlantic
island.

> *One or two crates stand on right of stage, one
> being big enough for a boy to hide in it.*
>
> *Near the front on the left grows one bush: others
> may be dotted about.*
>
> *As a rule pirates enter and exit left, children right.*

Act II, Scene 2 can be played in front of the curtain.

ACT I—

[*Enter* BEN, *left, kicked on, carrying crate. Puts down
crate, rubs himself, turns left and sticks out tongue.*]

BEN   Yah! Brute! Bully! Beast! Wait till I'm a
             man. I'll slit your gizzard and make you
             walk the plank. [*Staggers right with crate.*]
             [*Enter* TOUGH, *left, carrying two stools
             which he places right centre.*]

TOUGH   You'll get more of the same, my lad, if you
             don't act a bit more lively. Cap'n 'ull be
             here any minute. Get to work now and
             open that box. Mind you put the bottles
             in the shade. [*Calling back left.*] Hurry
             up with that clobber, you two.
             [*Enter* LOOPY *and* PATCH, *left, carrying
             more boxes and bundles. Come down
             centre looking round. Stand one on each
             side of* TOUGH.]

PATCH   Is this the place? H'm! Don't think much
             of it. Cap'n won't be best pleased.

TOUGH   It's the only place with shade and water
             this end of the island.

LOOPY   Why don't we go to the other end then?

PATCH   Hark at Loopy Bill! Go and ask the town-
             folk there to put us up in their spare
             rooms, I suppose.

LOOPY   Ain't this a desert island then?

TOUGH   No, it ain't, worse luck!

LOOPY   Then why did we come?

9

PATCH	I suppose you didn't notice the ship was leaking like a sieve, and that all hands to the pump only just kept her afloat till we got here?
TOUGH	And now we've beached her we'll be working the clock round till we get her afloat again, if I know the Cap'n.
PATCH	Might as well be measly sailors!
TOUGH	Can't be helped. Now, look slippy. Put the Cap'n's bedding out in those bushes and the other stuff with the drink. He said he'd be more comfortable away from the hammering and there'll be the deuce to pay if he don't find things ship-shape.

[LOOPY *goes right*, PATCH *across to* BEN *and the crates, where he leaves some gear, then across to* LOOPY. *They busy themselves preparing captain's bed.*]

[*Enter* CAPT. *and* MATE *left. Sit centre.* TOUGH, *after saluting, joins* BEN.]

CAPT.	This is a pretty pickle. Whoever heard of such awful luck? What's the shortest time you can get the repairs done in?
MATE	It will take all of three days I'm afraid, sir.
CAPT.	Three days! A pirate ship and a pirate crew within five miles of a thriving township, for three days!
MATE	But nobody could ever want to come to this end of the island, sir—dreary as it is—so it might be worse.
CAPT.	Don't be so foully optimistic. It couldn't be worse.
MATE	What about the prisoner, sir? She's shrieking her lungs out in the cabin.
CAPT.	Bad tempered little brat. Do her good.
MATE	But it makes the men uneasy, sir, and they don't work so well. Already they're saying that having a woman-creature on board is responsible for the Rake's having sprung a leak.
CAPT.	They'll pipe to a different tune when they get a share of the ransom money. Thank the pigs, we got the pinnace off with the

	demand note when we did. However, have it your own way. Bring her ashore and tell one of the hands off to watch her. Only she can't sleep here—I'm not having any squalling brats near me.
MATE	Here! You, Loopy. Go and fetch the prisoner here. Your job will be to keep an eye on her, and your neck will suffer if you let her slip. [*Exit* LOOPY.] [*To* CAPT.] Even he ought to be able to control a seven-year-old, and he won't be so much loss at the work as most.
CAPT.	You'll stay in the ship at nights, Mr. Mate. Let's see where these fellows have put my bedding. [*Goes left, followed by* TOUGH.] Whom have you detailed to wait on me, Bo'sun?
TOUGH	Patch, here, sir, and Ben, the boy. And Cook will be over to get your meals, Cap'n.
CAPT.	Where is that boy? Hi! Boy! A tot of rum for me and the Mate. Careful now. [*Re-seats himself.*] [BEN *serves both, but stops, staring left.*]
CAPT.	Now, what are you gaping at? Of all the doltish, lubberly young dogs!
BEN	P-please, C-Cap'n, here's the p-prisoner.
CAPT.	Well, what of it? I ——[*looks left*]. Jumping dog-fish! And this is the modern pirate! [*Enter* LOOPY, *driven by* SARAH *as horse, but sheepishly making efforts to restrain her. Stops by* CAPT.]
LOOPY	'Twas the only way to quieten her, Cap'n. She's a terrible screecher, she is, and when I got her from the cabin she was in a rare tantrum.
SARAH	[*peeping round* LOOPY *at* CAPT.] You're the naughty man who shut me up in the little room. You're *very* naughty.
CAPT.	[*standing and towering over* SARAH] It's you that's very naughty. And do you know what happens to naughty children in a pirate ship?

11

SARAH	No. What?
CAPT.	[*in a voice of doom*] They walk the plank.
SARAH	What's the plank?
CAPT.	Suffering jellyfish! It's a board that goes over the ship's side and ——
SARAH	Oh! That see-saw.
CAPT.	And when you walk it, you fall in the sea.
SARAH	With all your clothes on? How lovely! Let's go and do it now.
CAPT.	I give up! You can deal with her Mr. Mate. [*to pirates*] Come on, you dogs. Back to the ship. You're not spending the whole day idling here. [*Exit* CAPT., TOUGH, PATCH, *left.*]
MATE	No, boy, you stay. Understand Loopy? Keep your eye on her. No wandering. She means five thousand pieces of gold to us. You, boy. Finish unpacking those crates, then come back to the ship, pronto. [*Exit* MATE *left.*]
SARAH	[*to* LOOPY] Now, play with me.
LOOPY	[*looking at smirking* BOY, *suspiciously*] I can't play. [*to* BOY] Get back to your work.
SARAH	You can be my baby.
LOOPY	[*in agony*] I'm a *pirate*.
SARAH	Yes! A nice little pirate baby. And I'll put you to bed. Come over here [*goes to* CAPT'S. *bed*].
LOOPY	Well! I wouldn't mind a sit-down. Wait a minute. Boy, give me a noggin of rum.
BEN	It's the Cap'n's rum, Nursie.
LOOPY	You scallywag. [*catching* BEN *by ear and cuffing him*] A noggin of rum if you don't want any more. Make it two.
BEN	[*blubbering*] Can't you take a joke?
LOOPY	Not from the likes of you, I can't. Now, where's this here bed? [*to boy*] And if you so much as mention this to a soul, I'll—— [*draws finger across throat.*] [*Goes to* SARAH *and lies down and later sleeps.*]

12

SARAH	[*putting him to bed, covering him, etc.*] There, there! Don't cry. Nice and comfy. Don't throw the blanket off. Sh-Shush. [*Comes down centre.*] I'll make you a daisy chain if I can find any flowers. I'll have a comfit first—one that the Mate pirate gave me. [BEN *approaches* SARAH *and stands straddling and scowling at her.*]
SARAH	Hullo.
BEN	I'm a pirate.
SARAH	You're a very little pirate.
BEN	I've killed three men, I have.
SARAH	Have a comfit. [BEN *snatches all and crams them into his mouth.*]
SARAH	That's very greedy. And you shouldn't snatch.
BEN	That's what pirates do—take what they want.
ROBERT	[ROBERT'S *voice off right*] This way Priscilla. Come on. [BEN, *startled, rushes right and sees Robert's approach, rushes left and shakes* LOOPY *but fails to wake him.*]
BEN	Drunk! I must get to the ship and warn them.
PRISCILLA	[PRISCILLA'S *voice off left*] We're coming. Hurry up Alice.
ALICE	[ALICE'S *voice off left*] I'm coming as quickly as I can. Your legs are longer.
BEN	Cut off! Better hide. [*Hides in empty crate.*] [*Enter* ROBERT *right.* PRISCILLA *and* ALICE *left, all looking round, not seeing* SARAH.]
ROBERT	This is the place for the picnic. I told you —— [*sees* SARAH] Holy smoke! Who are you?
SARAH	I'm Sarah Miranda Courtier. Who are you?
ROBERT	Oh, we live the other end of the island. But you don't. How did you get here?
SARAH	In a ship.
PRISCILLA	Are you with your father and mother?

13

SARAH	No, father had to go on governing the island.
ALICE	What island?
SARAH	St Kitt's, of course, that he is governor of.
PRISCILLA	Then who is looking after you?
SARAH	The pirates are looking after me.
ROBERT	Gosh! Pirates! Do you mean you're their prisoner? What happened to——
PRISCILLA	[*quickly and warningly*] Robert! Come over here [*takes him left*]. Don't ask her what happened. It might remind her of all sorts of horrible things and upset her. She's probably being held for ransom. *We* must rescue her.
ROBERT	Jove, yes. Wait while I scout round and see if the coast is clear [*goes left*]. Look out! Here's one asleep. I'll just go and see if I can find any others or the ship. [*Exits left.*]
PRISCILLA	[*to* SARAH] Would you like to come home with us?
SARAH	My frock is very dirty.
ALICE	Oh, never mind that. We'll . . . [*breaks off as commotion is heard off left, then* ROBERT'S *voice calling.*]
ROBERT	[*voice*] Priscilla! Alice! Take Sarah and run. [PRISCILLA *and* ALICE *seize* SARAH'S *hands and run right but are confronted by* TOUGH, PATCH, *etc., who seize them.*] [LOOPY *scrambles up from his bed looking dazed and frightened.*]
TOUGH	No you don't, Missy.
PATCH	Now, now, young lady. Stop a bit and talk to the kind gentleman. [ALICE *bites his hand*] You young vixen, you. I'll . . . [*Enter* CAPT., MATE, BEN. MATE *holding* ROBERT.]
CAPT.	Loopy Bill! I'll talk to you in the morning. Meanwhile take the boy and those girls over there and keep tight hold of them. Boy, you may serve yourself a tot of rum. [*Pirates exit right with children, followed by* BEN *after he has had his drink.*]
CAPT.	It never rains but it pours. Of all the luck!

14

MATE	It certainly is serious, sir.
CAPT.	If we hold these—children—the island will be alive with search parties. If we let them go, they'll blab about the prisoner.
MATE	I suppose, sir, we couldn't make them promise silence and then let them go.
CAPT.	And why should they keep their promise once they're away?
MATE	Oh! Sir! If they give their word, I mean.
CAPT.	Eton and Harrow, eh? Well, we didn't all go there. I know I wouldn't keep mine in such a case.
MATE	[*demurely*] No, sir.
CAPT.	[*after suspicious look at* MATE] Not unless it paid me. I wonder . . . I might make a promise too.
MATE	Not meaning to keep it?
CAPT.	Of course not. But making it seem worth their while to keep mum. Offer them a reward.
MATE	They wouldn't take it, sir. Not children like that. They'd think it much more fun to rescue the prisoner.
CAPT.	What fools children are! Well then! Offer them the prisoner!
MATE	Give her up to them?
CAPT.	Not really, of course. But say they can have her after three days—on certain conditions.
MATE	What conditions?
CAPT.	Grinning skulls! Must you leave all the brain work to me? What was the good of your precious schooling, I'd like to know?
MATE	How would it be sir, to set them three tasks to be done to win the reward? They always do that in fairy tales.
CAPT.	Oh! So you read fairy tales, do you?
MATE	I used to before I went to school. You could spin them out till we were ready, even if they managed them, and then slope off. Though it seems rather a dirty trick.

15

CAPT.	Why you ever became a pirate, I don't know. Sort of modern Robin Hood, you are. What can we give them first?
MATE	Leave it to me sir. I'll tell them when you've explained the idea.
CAPT.	[*shouting right*] Tough. Here, all of you and bring the prisoners. [*Crosses left, followed by* MATE *bringing stools.*] [*Pirates bring children to face* CAPTAIN *and* MATE *who sit left centre.*]
CAPT.	Now, youngsters, you're in a pretty plight.
ROBERT	What are you going to do with us?
PRISCILLA	If you keep us, our father will rouse the town.
CAPT.	Indeed! I think my pirates could deal with a handful of islanders. However! I'm a sportsman! [*Crew snigger*] And I rather admire your attempt to rescue my prisoner, silly as it was.
ALICE	Let her come home with us then.
CAPT.	Well, my dear, I can hardly do that. I have told her father, for instance, that she is in my care.
ROBERT	Then what are you going to do?
CAPT.	There are lots of things I might do. You three, for example, might fall off that cliff over there. [*Girls squeak.*]
ROBERT	And when they found us they'd see your ship. We know you can't get her away yet.
CAPT.	[*snarling at pirates*] Numbskulls! You've been talking, have you? [*to children*] Or I might keep you here.
ROBERT	Same difficulty! They'd look for us.
CAPT.	[*snappily*] I've told you we could hold them off. But I always hate unnecessary bloodshed [*Crew guffaw*]. Or I could let you go.
PRISCILLA	But will you?
CAPT.	I might—on conditions.
ALICE	What do you mean?
CAPT.	I'd *rather* no one knew of our little lady Sarah here.

16

ROBERT	We're not going to promise to tell no one and let you carry her off if that's what you mean. It wouldn't be cricket.
CAPT.	Cricket! These oafish games! However! Supposing I was to make a sporting proposition. 'Twould help pass the time pleasantly.
ROBERT	What is it?
CAPT.	It's this. If you three will give me your words to say nothing about the prisoner or us in the meantime, I'll hand her over to you, provided that you can do three tasks that I shall set before we leave.
ALICE	Like the fairy tales.
CAPT.	That's what my Mate says. You have tastes in common.
ROBERT	You swear if we can do them, you'll give her to us?
CAPT.	Certainly, I swear.
ROBERT	What about it, Priscilla?
PRISCILLA	I say 'Yes'.
ALICE	It will be more fun this way.
CAPT.	The Mate will tell you the first task now.
MATE	[*rising*] You see this cummerbund I am wearing.
SARAH	Your sash, do you mean?
MATE	My cummerbund. Feel it. Lovely texture, isn't it? [*children finger it.*] Wonderful colour. Suits my complexion, I think.
PRISCILLA	Er—yes. It's a very nice cummerand,—cumberand.
MATE	Well! Your first task is to bring me another, *better* than the one I am wearing. [*Aside to* CAPT.] I happen to know they wear modern dress on this island and are not likely to have such a thing at all.
ROBERT	Shall we bring it here, when we've got it?
MATE	Yes. If you get it. The Captain will decide if it's better or not. [*Sarcastically*] He has such taste.
CAPT.	And remember—not a word about the prisoner till all three tasks are completed. We have your promise?

17

ALL	
CHILDREN	Yes.
CAPT.	We must go back to the ship now. Tough, bring the prisoner. [*Exit* CAPT. *and* MATE.]
TOUGH	Come along, Missy.
SARAH	I don't want to. I want to go with Robert.
PRISCILLA	Sarah! You shall come and stay with us for a long time if you're very good now. Anyhow, it's nearly your bed-time.
PATCH	And the cook will have got your supper ready, Missy.
SARAH	What is it?
PATCH	Pig's trotters.
SARAH	Ooh! Lovely! All right.
PRISCILLA	It ought to be bread and milk.
TOUGH	No such thing on a pirate ship. [*Exit pirates and* SARAH *left.*] [*Silence for minute while children look at each other.*]
ROBERT	It's not going to be so easy. It was a very fine cummerbund.
PRISCILLA	And we haven't got one anyway.
ALICE	Only my red sash.
PRISCILLA	That old thing. Why! It's all stained with juice where you spilt the strawberries.
ROBERT	And his looks brand new. Not a stain on it.
PRISCILLA	Coo! That's an idea. I wonder . . .
ROBERT AND ALICE	What?
PRISCILLA	He said 'better than his', didn't he?
ROBERT	Yes.
PRISCILLA	Well if his *happened* to get really badly torn or stained almost anything would be better. Alice's red sash, for instance.
ROBERT	You mean we could *make* it get torn and dirty.
PRISCILLA	Well, could we? It depends.
ROBERT	It's our only chance. We must think of a way. Let's get home and have a council of war. [*Exit right.*]

INTERVAL

ACT II—

SCENE I. *Next morning.*
[TOUGH *is standing left front by* BEN *who is sitting trussed like a chicken and blubbering. Raises rope's end.*] [*Enter* CAPT. *left, raging.*]

CAPT.   Skulls and little fishes! Where's that drink?

TOUGH   No wonder he didn't come when you called
                 for it, Cap'n. He was away off, almost
                 out of sight towards the other end of the
                 island.

CAPT.   Oh-ho! Perhaps our little Ben is tired of
                 being a pirate, eh, and wants to live in a
                 nice pretty house with white curtains and
                 daisies on the lawn? [BEN *blubbers.*]

TOUGH   [*grinning*] I've just reminded him with a
                 rope's end how fine a pirate's life is, and
                 I thought he'd better have a rest now in
                 the sun, to remind him how hot bad boys
                 get if they happen to die.

CAPT.   A pretty lesson. Let him stay there. I'll help
                 myself. [*Sits on bottle crate drinking, while*
                 TOUGH *watches him thirstily and is given a
                 drink after a time. They stay there during
                 children's entrance and conversation with*
                 MATE.] [MAINWARINGS *and* SARAH *enter
                 right,* ALICE *carrying ink bottle,* PRISCILLA
                 scissors and rope. Girls curtsey to CAPT.]

PRISCILLA   Good morning, Captain. Loopy let us have
                 Sarah. Robert is just going to fetch the
                 Mate from the ship. May he?

CAPT.   [*gloomily*] I suppose so. [*muttering*] Lot of
                 tomfoolery.

ROBERT   [*whispering*] Have you got everything ready?
                 [PRISCILLA *and* ALICE *nod and hold up
                 scissors and ink.*] Sarah, you're sure you
                 know what to do? [SARAH *nods.*] [*Exit*
                 ROBERT *left.*]

PRISCILLA   Now Sarah. We'll see if you really can skip.
                 [PRISCILLA *up stage,* ALICE *down stage,*
                 SARAH *on left.*]
                 [*to* ALICE] Keep a look out and tell me
                 when you see them. [SARAH *skips.*]

19

ALICE   Here they are.

PRISCILLA   Sarah, stand still there [*left.*] And hold on
                 tightly when he's down.
                 [*Enter* ROBERT. *Girls turn rope but lower
                 it to allow* ROBERT *to pass as he darts
                 forward.*]

ROBERT   I've got it here, sir, if you wouldn't mind
                 coming.
                 [*Enter* MATE.]
                 [*As* MATE *steps across rope to follow*
                 ROBERT, *girls tighten it. He trips and falls
                 on his hands and knees.* SARAH *pounces
                 high on his back calling 'Gee-up, Horsy!'*
                 ALICE *tilts bottle over his back.* PRISCILLA
                 *is on her knees snipping with scissors at
                 cummerbund.* MATE *remains helpless.*
                 CAPT. *and* TOUGH *guffaw.*]

MATE   Get her off, someone. For the love of mike!
                 Get her off.

PRISCILLA   [*lifting* SARAH *away*] [*sweetly*] He doesn't
                 want to play horses just now, Sarah. He
                 is going to look at the pretty sash we've
                 brought him.
                 [ALICE *and* ROBERT *help* MATE *to feet and
                 dust him down.*]

ROBERT   I'm so sorry, Mr. Mate. Really, girls! That
                 was very clumsy of you.

PRISCILLA   [*very earnestly*] Please forgive us, Mr. Mate.

MATE   I can forgive an accident like that quite
                 easily, Miss Priscilla. [*Looking at* CAPT.]
                 Though I can never understand the
                 people who laugh at others' misfortunes.

ROBERT   [*holding up rolled-up sash*] Here, Mr. Mate,
                 is your new cummerbund.
                 [*Unrolls rather faded, stained sash.*]

MATE   But, my dear boy! Is that the best you can
                 do? You don't really compare that thing
                 with *my* cummerbund, do you?

ROBERT   Captain, you were to be the judge. [CAPT.
                 comes forward centre between MATE *and*
                 ROBERT] Perhaps you would take yours
                 off so that we can see them together
                 properly, Mr. Mate.

20

MATE   [*snappily*] If you children are so blind as to think there could be any comparison I think I'd better. [*Unknots sash, holds it at arm's length and gazes in horror at slashed, inky ruin.*]

ROBERT   There Captain. Which would you say was the better cummerbund of the two?

CAPT.   [*maliciously*] Well! As a 'man of taste' I must admit yours is the one *I* should prefer to wear.

MATE   Of all the!!!!!!

ROBERT   Please take it then, Mr. Mate. [MATE *seizes Robert's sash, hurls it to the ground, grinds it with his heel, turns and stalks off left.*]

CAPT.   [*shaking his head*] Not a sportsman.

ROBERT   Then we have won the first round, Captain. What is the second task?

                [CAPT. *looks wildly after* MATE *and at* TOUGH, *but is interrupted by* SARAH *who, bored, has wandered off left front and is gazing down at* BEN.]

SARAH   Poor Ben! Why are you tied up like a parcel? [*Other children follow her.*]

ALICE   [*looking back at* CAPT.] Captain, what has he done?

CAPT.   Shirked his duty, the lubberly dog.

PRISCILLA   [*kneeling*] But he can't move an inch, poor boy, and he's burning hot. Mayn't I undo him?

CAPT.   You couldn't. He was tied by a seaman who knew his knots.

PRISCILLA   There certainly are a great many knots.

CAPT.   *There's* your second task. Set young Ben free from those knots and you're two-thirds of the way towards the reward. Only you'd better start soon if I know my Bo'sun, else you won't get it done before sun-down. I'll leave you to it.
                [*Exit left followed by* TOUGH.]

ROBERT   Well! Of all the luck!

PRISCILLA   What do you mean, Robert? I think it's awful. Wait a minute. Alice, fetch me our picnic flask. Are you thirsty, Ben?

21

BEN	[*blubbering*] Yes, miss! I wasn't doing anything. That there Tough . . .
PRISCILLA	Never mind. Drink this and you'll feel better and we'll see what we can do for you. Though I don't see how . . . [*shakes head sadly*] What did you mean by luck, Robert?
ROBERT	[*imitating schoolmaster*] Really! Miss Priscilla! Did you or did you not, attend my history lessons last term? [*In own voice*] I bet the Captain has never read history. Lucky the Mate had gone.
PRISCILLA	Robert! Of course! You mean the Gordian knot.
ROBERT	I do.
ALICE	[*almost wailing*] I wish someone would tell me what you're talking about. Do you mean you can undo him?
SARAH	[*patting* BEN] Poor Ben. Robert will undo you.
ROBERT	Alice, my child. The great Alexander set free a chariot knotted to a post as easily as winking, tho' thousands before him had tried to do it and failed. I shall do the same to Ben.
ALICE	But how?
ROBERT	[*getting out knife*] By cutting through the ropes.
BEN	Cor! *Cut* me free? The Cap'n won't half be mad. He meant you to undo all the knots.
PRISCILLA	He didn't *say* so.
ROBERT	Ben! Do you want to be set free?
BEN	Yes.
ROBERT	I don't know that you deserve it yet. After all, it was you that got us captured, wasn't it?
PRISCILLA	But he didn't know us then, did you Ben? You'd like to help us now, wouldn't you?
BEN	You gave me a drink, you did; I didn't know there was folk who'd be good to cabin boys.
ALICE	Do you *want* to be a pirate, Ben?
BEN	I dunno. There's nothing else for me to do.

22

ROBERT	Ben. If you'd come on to our side you could help a lot. And when the ship has to go, we'd rescue you as well as Sarah and my father would get you a job in the town.
BEN	But I'd 'ave to work.
PRISCILLA	Don't you have to work now?
BEN	Yus, I do. And for nothing but kicks and the rope's end.
PRISCILLA	Well then! And you could stay with us while you looked round.
BEN	Jiminy! I'm on then.
ROBERT	Come on. Let's waste no more time. The sooner we get this done, the more time we'll have for the third task. [*Saws* BEN *free.*]
SARAH	[*as* BEN *stretches himself*] Good little Ben. Not a parcel any more.
BEN	[*bashfully*] Funny little nipper, ain't she?
ROBERT	Come on all of you. A council of war. Here, Ben. You're one of us, now. [*All sit in semi-circle, facing audience*] We've got to find the Captain and get the third order. We've got to prove to him we've carried out the second but I don't think Ben ought to go near him yet awhile.
BEN	I don't mind. He'll knock me about, but he won't believe I'm free unless he sees me.
PRISCILLA	Ben, you're a hero. But he'll have to believe if he sees the ropes. So you hide till evening, Ben, and keep your eyes and ears open, and Robert and I will go and tell him and show him the ropes.
ALICE	No need. He's coming back.
ROBERT	Quick Ben. Off with you. [BEN *rushes off right.*] [*Enter* CAPT. *and* MATE *left,* CAPT. *in tearing rage.*]
CAPT.	Thunderation and thirty blue devils. It's cheating, that's what it is. The Mate saw you. Nothing but cheating. I said you'd got to undo the knots. Well, it doesn't count, that's all.
SARAH	He's a very naughty man. He's always in a temper.

CAPT.   Nothing of the sort. If you'd been cheated out of five thousand pieces of gold . . .

MATE   The point is, sir—did you precisely say 'undo the knots'?

CAPT.   [*bitterly*] Whose side are you on? How should I remember my actual words?

ALICE   He said, 'set him free'.

MATE   [*looks enquiringly at the others*] Did he? [ROBERT *and* PRISCILLA *nod.*]

MATE   I'm afraid the verdict goes against you sir. [CAPT. *crosses to left, sulking.*]

ROBERT   What is the third task, Mr Mate? We'll have to go home soon and there's only to-morrow. You'll be going the next day, won't you?

MATE   Who told you that? Oh! Never mind. If you'll excuse me, I'll consult the Captain. I'm not sure whether he has made up his mind yet. [*Crosses left to* CAPT. *while children go right. They picnic while* CAPT. *and* MATE *talk.*] [BEN *enters left, sees* CAPT. *and* MATE, *starts back but hides in bushes near them, listening.*]

MATE   Sir! A stroke of luck for us!

CAPT.   About time too! If I'd known what brats could be like I'd have scuppered them and risked the results.

MATE   They think, sir, that they've got till the day after to-morrow. Nobody has told them we shall be ready to-morrow night.

CAPT.   I should hope not!

MATE   I take it you have decided on their third task?

CAPT.   I'm not leaving it to you again after your first fiasco.

MATE   [*stiffly*] I beg your pardon, sir, but your own was hardly more successful.

CAPT.   That was only because of this modern foolishness of teaching brats history! Nobody could foresee that.

MATE   Well! What I was going to say was this. If, by any chance, they succeed in their third trial—

24

CAPT.	They won't.
MATE	[*suavely*] I'm sure of it, sir. But if they did, we could still bamboozle them.
CAPT.	How!
MATE	Why, sir, you can pretend to be a sportsman again and adopt a 'Best Man Wins' sort of attitude, but appeal to their reason.
CAPT.	Have they any?
MATE	Oh, yes, sir. Children are quite reasonable animals. Point out to them that it would be too dangerous for us to hand over the prisoner at once, but that you would do it first thing *the next* morning before we sail.
CAPT.	And sail off with her to-morrow night! Mr Mate, I believe you're a real pirate after all. That's a beautiful dirty trick. All the same, it won't be necessary. You listen. [*calling to children*] Ready? [*Children cross to centre.*]
ROBERT	With the third task, Captain?
CAPT.	Yes, listen. In your town there lives an old sailor.
ALICE	Yes, lots.
CAPT.	Don't interrupt. When I was young I was taught it was bad manners.
ALICE	[*genuinely astonished*] Were you?
CAPT.	[*glaring at her*] One particular old sailor whom I used to know, though he was only a sailor and not a 'gentleman of fortune'.
ROBERT	[*aside to* ALICE] A pirate.
CAPT.	If you can find that old sailor he will tell you the name that he tattooed on my chest. That is your task—to tell me that name. And it's no use guessing; you'll never get it that way.
PRISCILLA	[*dismayed*] But we don't even know your name. [BEN *exits stealthily.*]
CAPT.	A pity! But I can't help you any more. I should get back home and begin looking for the sailor. Good afternoon. [*Exit left, followed by* MATE'S *really admiring look.*]

MATE	He *has* set you a teaser this time. I must get back to work too. Come, Sarah. I've got some more comfits in the cabin.
SARAH	Good-bye, Robert. I'll bring you some of them to-morrow. Good-bye, Priscilla. 'Bye, Alice. [*Exit* MATE *and* SARAH *left.*]
PRISCILLA	What *shall* we do? I think that's finished us.
ALICE	[*beginning to wail*] We *can't* let Sarah go with them.
ROBERT	Be quiet you two and *think*. Come back to the ponies. [*All exit right.*] [*A moment's pause.*] [BEN, *looking fearfully over shoulder, creeps on left, looks round and hurries after children.*]

SCENE II. *Another part of the Scrub. In front of the curtain. An hour later.*

[*Enter* ROBERT *right, looking worried and peering ahead.* BEN *runs after him, panting.* ROBERT *turns round, relieved.*]

ROBERT	I've been hunting for you all over the place.
BEN	I've been lookin' for you, too. I heard them two.
ROBERT	The Mate and the Captain?
BEN	Yus. Before they told you your last job.
ROBERT	Good. That saves my explaining.
BEN	But it don't save me. I 'eard wot you didn't. They mean to *do* you, diddle you.
ROBERT	How?
BEN	Even if you get the name they'll say they can't hand over the nipper till the next morning. And—the ship sails to-morrow *night*.
ROBERT	My stars! Are you sure? [BEN *nods*] Well! I didn't think even pirates . . . The Mate too?
BEN	It was 'im wot thought of it, for all 'is lah-de-dah ways.
ROBERT	The utter beast.

26

BEN	Wot you goin' to do?
ROBERT	[*thinking it out*] We must keep *our* words anyway.
BEN	Not peach, you mean?
ROBERT	Not till we've done the job. Then, I *think*, if we're certain they're going to cheat, we've got the right to take our reward for ourselves, any way we can.
BEN	Cor!
ROBERT	But we *must* do the job first. And we need your help, Ben.
BEN	I'm for you.
ROBERT	It may be dangerous.
BEN	I'm game.
ROBERT	Listen then. We came on the ponies to-day, luckily. Priscilla and Alice have gone on home to fetch something. Priscilla is bringing it back.
BEN	Wot is it?
ROBERT	Something for you to put in the Captain's drink.
BEN	[*awed*] Poison?
ROBERT	No. Serve him right if it were. Something to make him sleep very very soundly. My father's a doctor and he told me about it because I'm going to be one too. Can you give it to him in his last drink to-night?
BEN	Easy. But why?
ROBERT	There's not a hope of finding that sailor and he knows it. But, if we wait till he's dead asleep we might be able to see the name itself.
BEN	My! You are a one for thinking of things.
ROBERT	Ben. You must pretend to be against us and sorry about this morning or they might suspect.
BEN	Right.
ROBERT	Come now to where I left my pony. Priscilla ought to be there. The sooner you're back at the camp, the better. I hope they won't be too beastly to you.
BEN	They will be, but it won't be for long now.

27

ACT III—

SCENE I. *Just before dawn.*

[CAPT. *asleep, up left.* BEN *is moving about quietly and watching right.*]

[*Enter* ROBERT *right, stealthily. He and* BEN *move down right and talk in whispers.*]

BEN 'Ere you are! Alone?

ROBERT Yes. I wouldn't let the girls come. Priscilla wanted to.

BEN I bet she did. Real spunky, she is.

ROBERT Is everything all right?

BEN Fine. He's dead off. I've even dropped things and he hasn't stirred. I persuaded 'im to give me 'is coat to brush so 'e's in 'is shirt-sleeves.

ROBERT Well done, Ben!

BEN And I've got the lantern ready, so we can see.

ROBERT You think of things too, don't you, Ben? Come on, then. Let's get it over.

[*Boys move quietly over to* CAPT., BEN *carrying lantern. Kneel down either side of him. Gently* ROBERT *turns back the blankets.* CAPT. *stirs and boys sit back.* ROBERT *tickles* CAPT'S. *throat with feather and* CAPT., *still asleep, claws at his shirt.*]

ROBERT That's it, Ben. Hold the lantern up but don't let it shine in his eyes.

[*Boys bend over* CAPT.'S *chest. Suddenly sit back with hands over mouths, stifling giggles.* ROBERT *motions* BEN *right, both still suppressing laughter.*]

BEN Whoever 'ud have thought it?

ROBERT Nobody! We wouldn't have guessed in a thousand years. Now, Ben, listen! I can't tell you exactly what is planned, but we've done our share of the bargain and we've got a right to Sarah. If the Captain cheats, the bargain's off. You're sure, aren't you, that he's going to?

BEN Sure as I'm standing 'ere.

28

ROBERT	Very well. We'll take her then. Don't be worried if you don't see us till well on in the afternoon. But, if you can, be with Sarah and ready to do what we tell you.
BEN	I'll keep an eye on the nipper.
ROBERT	And whatever happens to the others, remember you're one of us and are perfectly safe.
BEN	One of you! Cor!
ROBERT	[*going up right*] Good-bye for now, watch out for us and keep an eye on things.
BEN	Aye-Aye, partner.
	[*Exit* ROBERT *right.*]
	[BEN *looks after him, turns back towards* CAPT. *and stands looking down at him with a triumphant grin.*]

SCENE II. *Captain's Camp. Late afternoon.*

[CAPT. *and* MATE *sit left centre, drinking.* TOUGH *and* PATCH *are rolling and lashing bedding on left.* LOOPY, SARAH, BEN *are packing crates, right.*]

CAPT.	Not a sign of them. They're running round the town talking to all the old sailors. [*Chortles evilly.*]
MATE	Well! I must hand it to you, sir. It was a very tidy scheme.
CAPT.	Bo'sun, are those duds nearly ready?
TOUGH	Aye-Aye, Cap'n. We're off at the turn of the tide, then?
CAPT.	We are that, my lad. Boy, you may serve the hands a tot apiece before you fasten up that last crate. [*Crew cheer.*]
SARAH	[*running to* CAPT. *and* MATE] Here's Robert, Captain, and Priscilla and Alice.
CAPT.	[*rising*] Where? They can't . . . No! Look at them, Mr Mate. They've come to say they've failed. Rich, eh?
	[*Enter* ROBERT, ALICE *and* PRISCILLA *slowly with hanging heads.* SARAH *runs to* PRISCILLA *who takes her hand but says nothing. They face* CAPT. *while crew watch them.*]

29

CAPT.	Well, my hearties, did you find the sailor?
ALICE	I don't believe there was such a sailor.
CAPT.	[*calmly*] There wasn't.
PRISCILLA	Then it wasn't fair. That's not keeping to the bargain.
ROBERT	My father says that if a bargain is not kept by *both* sides, neither side is bound by it.
CAPT.	[*still calm*] Quite! If I've broken the pact, you have no need to keep your promise. But I haven't.
MATE	Better explain to the poor children, Cap'n.
CAPT.	The task I set wasn't to find the sailor. It was to tell me the name tattooed on my chest.
ROBERT	Oh! We can do that.
CAPT.	What!
ROBERT	Shall I tell it?
CAPT.	[*looking round wildly*] No. Yes. No.
MATE AND CREW	Yes. Tell it.
ROBERT	It is—Primrose.
	[MATE *and* CREW *look aghast at* CAPT. *and then are overcome by mirth.*]
CAPT.	It's witchcraft. That's what it is! Witchcraft! Not a soul knew.
MATE	[*silkily*] May we see if he is right, sir?
CAPT.	No, you may not. [*to children*] You needn't think you are going to get away . . .
MATE	[*urgently*] Sir! Sportsman, sportsman!
CAPT.	[*taken aback and confused, but pulls himself together and grins falsely*] Well, I don't know how you did it but I'm afraid it's a case of 'the best man wins'.
	[*Looks for approval at* MATE *who nods encouragingly.*]
PRISCILLA	So, we may take Sarah home now?
CAPT.	You shall certainly have her. But as sportsmen and sportswomen, you can see that her appearance in your town to-night would lead to enquiries and we might be stopped from leaving in the morning.
	[ROBERT *and* BEN *nod to each other as much as to say 'I told you so'.*]

ROBERT	You don't leave till morning then?
CAPT.	[*while* PRISCILLA *and* SARAH *cross to* PATCH *and* TOUGH *and* ALICE *to* LOOPY] Alas, no!
PRISCILLA	Why are you rolling the Captain's bedding, Patch?
PATCH	[*startled, with his eye on the* CAPT.] Cap'n thought he'd sleep on board the last night, miss. [CAPT. *having listened anxiously, sighs in relief.* PRISCILLA *and* SARAH *exit.*]
ALICE	I've got a present for you, Loopy.
LOOPY	Ooh, Miss! [*holds out his hand*].
ALICE	No, not now. To-morrow, before you go.
LOOPY	[*greedily*] Better now, Miss.
ALICE	Why? Are you going *before* to-morrow?
LOOPY	Yus, Miss. To-night. [*gazes affrighted at* CAPT.] [*Exit* ALICE.] [CAPT. *taking vicious stride towards* LOOPY, *is stopped by* ROBERT. BEN *comes up behind* ROBERT.]
ROBERT	We knew it already Captain. That was only the last proof. You were cheating.
CAPT.	[*sneering*] What of it? Only stupid brats would expect anything else of pirates.
ROBERT	We know better now. Pirates can't be gentlemen, not even when they've been to public schools.
CAPT.	And what do you propose to do about it? We'll be off in an hour with your little friend and you can do nothing. Ha!
ROBERT	We've done it. We kept our side of the bargain. We kept silence till we'd done the three tasks you set and would have kept silence till you'd got clear away if Ben hadn't told us of your dirty trick.
CAPT.	Oh-ha, Master Ben! We've you to thank for this. I'll thank you when I've got you on board. And that will be at once.
ROBERT	Oh, no it won't. By now the girls have given the signal. [CAPT. *and* MATE *look round.*]
CAPT.	The girls?
MATE	Where are they?

31

CAPT.	What signal?
ROBERT	The signal to the townsfolk whom our father collected after we told him—when we knew you were cheating.
CAPT.	You young rip. Well I'll do for you, anyway. [*raises dagger threateningly but stops to listen to* ROBERT.]
ROBERT	[*blanching and stepping back but still brave*] I shouldn't. Every man of you is covered. Anyone who moves is a dead man.
MAN'S VOICE	[*off stage right*] The boy's right. Every man jack of you put your hands above your heads.
	[*Pirates raise arms slowly.*]
	Now! Move to command.
	[ROBERT *and* BEN *move up centre and are joined by girls who come on left.*]
	The crew first.
	[*Crew file off singly, right,* TOUGH *kicking* LOOPY *off stage in front of him.*]
	Now the Mate.
	[MATE *assumes a jaunty air. As he passes children he even attempts a bow, to which the girls, though startled, respond by bobbing.*]
MATE	[*as he passes* BEN] Rat!
MAN'S VOICE	Now 'Captain'.
	[CAPT. *glances wildly round but yields and slowly moves right. Before going off, however, he turns round to children who have moved up stage, and snarls.*]
	[ALICE *hides her face on* PRISCILLA'S *shoulder.* SARAH *looks up at* PRISCILLA *wonderingly.* ROBERT *looks at* CAPT. *squarely. But* BEN *sticks out his tongue as far as it will go, and only when* PRISCILLA *shakes her head at him reprovingly claps his hand over his mouth and looks shamefaced.*]

CURTAIN